A Great Day Out!

Barbara Mitchelhill

Published in association with
The Basic Skills Agency

Hodder & Stoughton

A MEMBER OF T

Acknowledgements
Cover: Lee Stinton
Illustrations: Jim Eldridge

Orders: please contact Bookpoint Ltd, 39 Milton Park, Abingdon, Oxon OX14
4TD. Telephone: (44) 01235 400414, Fax: (44) 01235 400454. Lines are open
from 9.00–6.00, Monday to Saturday, with a 24 hour message answering
service. Email address: orders@bookpoint.co.uk

British Library Cataloguing in Publication Data
A catalogue record for this title is available from The British Library

ISBN 0 340 74322 0

First published 1999
Impression number   10 9 8 7 6 5 4 3 2
Year   2004 2003 2002 2001 2000 1999

Copyright © 1999 Barbara Mitchelhill

Typeset by by Fakenham Photosetting Ltd, Fakenham, Norfolk.
Printed in Great Britain for Hodder & Stoughton Educational, a division of
Hodder Headline Plc, 338 Euston Road, London NW1 3BH by Athenaeum
Press Ltd, Gateshead, Tyne & Wear.

About the play

The People

- **Dean**
- **Lee**

What's Happening

*Outside a large comprehensive school, Years 8 and 9 are waiting to board a coach for a school trip. **Dean** approaches **Lee** and persuades him to bunk off the trip.*

Outside a large comprehensive school.

Dean Pssst! Lee!
Over here!
Quick!

Lee What do you want, Dean?
I'm going to catch the coach.

Dean You're not going anywhere.
(*He grabs Lee's collar*)
We'll give the school trip a miss.
We're going to have
a great day out.

Lee Doing what?

Dean Loads of things. Wait and see.

Lee I – I don't know, Dean.
I wanted to see the castle.

Dean Castles are dead boring.
Writing notes and all that. Yuk!
Forget it. Come on.
We're going to have a great day.

Lee	We'll get into trouble.
	They'll know we're missing.
Dean	Trust me!
	I've got a great plan.
	They won't miss us.
	We weren't on the class list.
Lee	How come?
Dean	Because I rubbed our names out.
	Miss Hunt left the list on
	her desk. I got it when nobody
	was looking.
	Our names are wiped out.
Lee	Smart one, Dean!
	But I still want to go on
	the trip.
	I want to see the dungeons.
	I've been looking forward to it.
Dean	(*Twisting Lee's arm*)
	And what if I say you can't?
Lee	Aaaaggghhh!
	You're hurting me Dean.

Dean   Are you coming then?

Lee   Do I have to?

Dean   Yeah!

Lee   Aaaggghhh! OK. I'll come.

Dean   Right then.

Part one of my Great Plan.

We go to the bike shed.

We'll hide out of the rain, eh?

Lee   Right, Dean.

They run down to the bike shed.

Dean   Come in quick, Lee.
Shut the door behind you.
Keep the rain out.

They shut the door.

Lee   Cor – it's really dark in here.
I can't see a thing.
And it smells.

Dean   It's a laugh, ain't it?
I bet the others aren't having
this much fun.
They'll all be sitting on
the coach waiting to go.
Miss Hunt will be telling 'em
to get out their books.

Lee   I bet it's nice and warm in
the coach.
I bet they don't have rain
dripping in.

Dean	Who cares about being warm?
	You're a wimp, Lee!
	We're going to have a great
	day out.
Lee	How long do we stay here?
	What's part two of your plan?
Dean	We wait till the coach leaves.
	Then we can go.
Lee	(*Sighs*)
	That could be ages.
	I'm bored.
	Can't we do something?
Dean	We could do keep fit.
	See that beam up there?
Lee	Yeah!
Dean	We'll jump up and hang.
	Then we'll do pull-ups.
	Dead easy if you've got muscles
	like mine.
Lee	Go on then.
	You show me, Dean.

Dean   OK. Here I go.
Watch me!

Dean jumps up and begins his pull-ups.

Lee   Are those pull-ups, Dean?
You're not moving much.

Dean   Oooh! Aaaggghhh!
It's dead hard ...
Up ... er ... Aaaggghhh!
Ow!

Dean crashes to the floor.

Lee   Are you all right, Dean?

Dean   Do I look all right?
I think I've broken my arm.
Aaaggghhh!

Lee	Shall we forget about your plan?
	We've still got time to catch
	the coach.
Dean	Sit on a coach for hours?
	You must be joking.
	Dead boring!
	My bum will get cramp, won't it?
Lee	But we'll be walking round the
	castle later.
	Looking at the dungeons.
	They're dead good!
Dean	We don't want to go to that
	old ruin!
	Walking round taking notes?
	Having to write about it for
	homework?
	We're well out of it.
Lee	Well ... I suppose so.
	Anything to get out of
	homework.

Dean	We can do anything we like. All day. Anything.
Lee	Yeah! Anything we like … Er … what was this great idea of yours, Dean?
Dean	Something dead exciting.
Lee	Like what?
Dean	I'll think of something. We've got to get out of this shed first. I'll just look and see if the coach is still there.

Dean pushes open the door and peeps out.

Lee	What can you see, Dean? Have they left?

Dean   They're going now.
The coach is going down
the drive.

Lee   Can we come out of the
shed then?

Dean   Er ... not just yet.
Wait till the rain stops.
If we walk into town now,
we'll get soaked.
It'll stop soon.

Lee	OK, then. But this is boring.

*Lee starts walking backwards
and forwards counting.
1 ... 2 ... 3 ... 4 ...*

Dean	What are you doing?
Lee	I'm seeing how long the bike shed is. We do it in maths sometimes.
Dean	Well, don't! You're driving me nuts.
Lee	I've got to do something. I can't just stand here.
Dean	We could tell jokes.
Lee	All right then. Go on. You start. I don't know any.
Dean	I know a brilliant one. I'll tell you. There was this dog standing in the road.

Lee Dogs don't stand in the
middle of roads.

Dean Well this dog did.
Now shut up and listen.
There was this dog and it
was crying.

Lee That's daft. Dog's don't cry.
No way!

Dean SHUT UP, LEE.
IT'S A JOKE.
There was this dog and it was
crying and this bloke said,
'What's up?' And the dog said,
'I've got a very nice owner
who takes me for walks.
And I have plenty of bones.'

Lee Dogs needs more than bones,
Dean. They need meat.
I bet it was fed up because it
didn't get meat.

Dean	LISTEN, LEE, WILL YOU?
Lee	Right, I'll shut up. Carry on, Dean.
Dean	There was this dog in the middle of the road ...
Lee	You said all that.

Dean grabs hold of Lee by the collar.

Dean   I know I said it.
I was starting again.
And if you say another word,
I'll thump you. RIGHT?

Lee   (*Nods and makes noises
as he is afraid to speak.*)
Mmm … mmm … mmm

Dean   There was a dog
and it was crying.
This man asked him what
was wrong.
The dog said, 'I've got a nice
owner who takes me for walks.
I have loads of bones and meat.
I've got a bed with plenty
of soft blankets.'
So the bloke said, 'You've got
everything a dog could want.
Why are you crying?'
The dog said, 'I'm crying 'cos
I can't find my way home.'
Good joke, eh, Lee?

Lee	(*Nodding*)
	Mmmm … mmmm … mmmm.
Dean	It's OK. You can speak now.
Lee	Cool, Dean. Really cool.
Dean	Brilliant, eh?
Lee	I've just remembered.
Dean	Just remembered what?
Lee	I've remembered a joke. Listen. Where does a vampire keep his money?
Dean	SSSSHHH!
Lee	I haven't finished yet.
Dean	SSSSHHH!
	I can hear something.

Footsteps can be heard outside the shed.

| **Lee** | (*Whispering*) |
| | You're right! Sounds like somebody with big boots. |

Dean Hide in the corner
in case he comes in.
It could be Old Barnet.
I bet he's come to check the bikes.

Sound of hammering at the door.

What's he doing?

Hammering.

Dean He's nailing something on
the door.

*Hammering stops and footsteps
recede into the distance.*

That's lucky. He's gone.
Let's go and see what he's done.
Lee (*Rattling door*)
It won't open, Dean. It's locked.

Dean   I expect it's just stuck.
Let me try. You're a real wimp.
You want to build up your
muscles, you do.

Dean *rattles door.*

It won't open!
He's fixed some kind of
lock on it.

Lee   Some of the bikes were nicked
last term.
I expect that's why he did it.

Dean   Yeah! And just our luck that he
did it today. Now I'm stuck
in here with you until he comes
back and unlocks it.

Lee   At four o'clock.

Dean   Yeah! All day.
I don't believe it! Just when
I'd got our day planned.

Lee   You never told me what it was.

Dean   What's the point?
We can't do it now.

Lee   Go on. Tell me what you'd
got planned.

Dean   Well ... we were going to go
into town and buy hot dogs.

Lee   That sounds great!

Dean	Then we were going to go to the pictures and have ice-creams.
Lee	Brilliant! I'll have mint and chocolate chip ... with toffee sauce.
Dean	There's a brilliant film on about this thing from another planet. This boy finds it and it's crying ...
Lee	It's not a dog, is it?
Dean	No it's not a dog. They don't have dogs in outer space.
Lee	Good. Then you won't be able to tell that joke again. What were we going to do after we'd seen that film about the cat from outer space?
Dean	It wasn't a cat either, stupid! After the film, we were going to go to the funfair.

Lee   Cool! I think funfairs
are fantastic.
Er ... the only thing is ...
I haven't got any money.

Dean   No problem! I've got loads!
I was going to pay for you.
We could have gone on all
the rides. Money's no problem.

Lee   But we can't go to the funfair
because we're stuck in here.

Dean   So much for our day out.
I knew it was a bad idea.
Didn't I say so?
Didn't I say it was a bad idea?

Lee   It was *your* idea.

Dean   Oh yeah. You would say that.

Lee   Because it's true.

Dean Yes. Well … I'm the only one
who ever has ideas.
You never have anything in your
brain except cotton wool.

Lee I've got an idea now.

Dean Oh yeah?

Lee See that corner of the shed?

Dean Yeah.

Lee That plank of wood.
There's a nail missing.

Dean So?

Lee It won't take much to pull
it away. Make a hole.
Maybe we could make a hole
big enough to get through.

Dean Says you!

Lee We could try.

Dean No. *I'll* try.
You're a wimp. A real weed.
You couldn't rip out that plank
of wood. No way.
Stand back. I'll do it.

*Sounds of grunting and groaning
as **Dean** pulls on the wood.*

OWWW!

***Dean** jumps about sucking
his finger.*

Lee What have you done, Dean?
Stop jumping about.
Let me look.

Dean	My finger. AGGGHHH!
	It's killing me.
	That wood's rotten.
	AGGGHHH!
	I need a doctor.
Lee	(*Grabbing **Dean**'s hand*)
	I can fix it.
	It's a splinter, that's all.
Dean	That's all? That's all?
	What would you know about it?
	I'm not touching that wood again.
	You'll have to do it.
Lee	OK. I'll give it a go.

Grunting and groaning as
***Lee** pulls on the wood.*

Ah! Got it.

It's coming away. Easy. Great!

We've got our hole. Look.

Dean	Call that a hole?
	You couldn't push a sandwich
	through it.
Lee	So we'll have to take out some
	more planks.
	The others should come off easy.
	Stand back and I'll try.

Grunting and groaning as
Lee *pulls on the wood.*

Ah! Another one!

More grunting and groaning.

And again. Three planks.
We can get through that hole.
Why are you standing there, Dean?
Don't you want to get out?

Dean	'Course I do.

Lee	Cool! I can't wait to get
	down town.
	I can almost taste those hot dogs
	and that film sounds great.
	Let's get going or we won't
	have time to go to the funfair.
Dean	Well ... have you got any money?
Lee	You said you'd got plenty.
Dean	(*Feeling in his pocket*)
	I've got a hole in my pocket.
	I must have lost it.
Lee	Oh yeah?
	That's a joke. Right, Dean?
	Let's get moving. You go first.
	I'm a wimp. You said so, remember?
Dean	I'd like to but my hand feels
	really bad.
Lee	You mean you can't do it?

Dean	Er ... I can do it!
	'Course I can do it!
	Watch me!

Dean pushes his way through the hole.

	AGGGHHH! I'm stuck!
	Lee! I've got a nail in my bum.
	Help me, will you?
	AGGGHHH! I'm in agony.
Lee	Don't be a wimp, Dean.
	Hold on. I'll give you a push.

Lee pushes Dean, screaming in pain.
Dean lands on the ground
on the outside of the bike shed.

Dean   Oh no! I'm bleeding.

And my trousers …

They're ripped. They're ruined.

Mum'll kill me.

Lee   (*Laughing*)

I can see a massive hole, Dean.

I can see your bum through it!

Dean   I can't go down town, can I?

Not now.

Lee   Aren't you going to buy me a

hot dog, Dean?

Dean   You've made a mess of everything!

I wouldn't buy you a hot dog

if you were my last mate.

I'm going home.

Lee	I've got a better idea.
	I'm going back to school and
	I'll tell them I've over-slept.
	That way all I'll get
	is a telling off.
Dean	I'll come with you.
Lee	No way. They never believe you.
	You look as if you've been
	in a fight.
	I know what you should do.
Dean	What?
Lee	Go home to Mummy and tell her
	about your great day out!